THE THREE BEARS

Once upon a time there were three  who lived in a deep in the . There was a great big papa bear ; there was a middle-sized mama bear , and there was a little boy baby bear . One fine morning, made some porridge for

breakfast. She poured it into
three 🍲🍲🍲 to cool. Then
the 🐻🐻🐻 went out for a
long walk in the 🌳🌳.

While they were gone, a pretty little named Goldilocks came to the of the . She knocked at the . Nobody answered, so little pushed open the and went inside.

She saw the with the three on it and with the three beside

them   just   as      had
left   them.   Now      was
feeling   hungry,   so   she
tasted   the   porridge   in   the
big   .   It   was   too   hot.

She tasted the porridge in the middle-sized 🥣 It was too cold. She tasted the porridge in the little 🥣. It was just right!

Then 👧 saw three 🪑🪑🪑. There was a big 🪑 which belonged to 🐻, a middle-sized 🪑 which belonged to 🐻 and a little 🪑 which belonged to 🐻

 sat down in the

big 🪑 . It was too hard.

Then she sat down on the

middle-sized 🪑 . It was

too soft. When she sat on

the little 🪑 , she found

it was just right.

But, oh dear! 👧 was

much too big and heavy

for such a little 🪑 . It

went crashing to the hard

🟫 with the startled

little 👧 , and it broke in-

to little bits and 🪵 .

👧 picked herself up off

the 🟫 and decided to

see what was up .

She found 3  that

belonged to the  .

 was sleepy so she

climbed up on the big

to rest. The was too high to suit her. Then she lay down on the middle-sized . The was too low. Next she crawled into the little . It felt just right! Soon was fast asleep.

When the returned to their , looked at his with the

turned over next to it,
and said in his great big
voice, "Somebody has been

eating my porridge!"

 looked at her

with the  still in it
and said in her middle-
sized voice, "Somebody has
been eaten my porridge."
looked at his  ,

and cried in his squeaky
little voice, "Somebody has
been eating my porridge,
too—and has eaten every
bit! My is empty."
looked at his
and cried out in his great
big voice, "Somebody has
been sitting in my ."
Then looked at her
and saw that the soft

red  had been moved.

"And somebody has been sitting in my , too." she said in her middle-sized voice.

Then 🐻 looked for

his 🪑. All he saw was

bits and 🪑💥 of it on

the kitchen 🟫. He rubbed

the 💧💧 from his 👀 with

his little brown 🐾 and

said in his squeaky little

voice, "Somebody has been

sitting in my 🪑, too, and

has broken it all to 💥🪑."

The 🐻🐻🐻 looked all

over the room, under the
and in the where they
hung their . But they
couldn't find anyone. Then
they went up to look
in the bedroom.

 looked at his [bed] and saw that his [blanket] were rumpled and his [pillow] was mussed. He called out in his deep voice, "Somebody has been sleeping in my [bed]."

Then [bear] looked at her [chair] and said in her middle-sized voice, "Somebody has been sleeping in my [bed]."

Then [bear] went over to his

little  and he looked and could hardly believe his 👀 . Finally, said in his squeaky little voice, "Some-body has been sleeping in my and HERE SHE IS!"

 and rushed over to the little  . They, too, could hardly believe their 👀 👀 ! There was sleeping in the

with her golden all

spread over the

whispered, "Is she

a real little ?" put

out his to touch her,

but just then opened

her and saw the

standing there.

"Oh, goodness me!"

cried out, and she jumped

out of the little and

ran down the  as fast
as she could. Through the
front and out of the
and down the